INTO THE WIND...

A mustang's story

Written and illustrated
by Susan Metcalfe Hennes

Into the Wind

ISBN 978-1-7372970-1-7

Names, characters, and some of the places are products of the author's imagination.

Front cover image and illustrations by the author.
Book design by Andrea Reider at Reider Books
Published in the United States of America
First printing edition 2021

Visit the author's website www.meadowbrookgallery.com

Written for all those horses who allowed me to peek into their souls and with whom I have shared so many precious hours. I will forever be in their debt.

Susan Metcalfe Honneus

CHARACTERS IN THE BOOK...

JERRY MCMAHON	Long haul truck driver
JAKE STREETER	Young boy who first chased the horses
TOM CONNELLY	Jake's companion in the chase
ROOSEVELT BROWN	Prison inmate who halter-broke Darius
LESTER BIDWELL	Grandfather who bought Darius at the BLM auction
TAYLOR BIDWELL	Lester's granddaughter
BEN CLAYTON	Trainer who tried to break Darius to saddle
TED "SCOOTER" HARRINGTON	Owner of the Roaring Reality Rodeo
RUNNING FEATHER (EARL)	Lakota American who befriended Darius
JEREMY COGGINS	Rodeo rider
TASUNKA	Lakota legend word for horse

CONTENTS

According to Bedouin legend, "Allah took a handful of southerly wind, blew His breath over it, and created the horse."

CHAPTER ONE

BEGINNINGS

The heavily pregnant mare grazed near the edge of a small band of horses on the high plateau.[1] Beneath a vast expanse of sky, a chilly, early spring breeze held the promise of warmer days to come. She moved slowly at first, savoring the sweet, tender shoots of the new

---

[1] Plateau: a high plain or an area of highland, usually consisting of relatively flat terrain that is raised significantly above the surrounding area, often with one or more sides with steep hills.

spring grasses growing at her feet. She lingered for a time in the company of the other horses until she began to feel an urgency within. As this feeling grew stronger, she drifted further and further away from the herd.

When she could no longer ignore the pressure in her belly, she lifted her head, sniffed the air, and turned toward an embankment that led down to a thin wash below. With one last look at the others, she moved with purpose along a narrow path that led down the side of the bluff. A small black stallion raised his head as she moved away. His eyes and hearing were sharp and clear beneath a ragged mane that blew wildly about his head. He watched her go but did nothing to reclaim her, sensing her purpose.

She picked her way cautiously down the path, burdened by her large belly, placing her hooves carefully between the stones on the trail. Once down on level ground, she headed for the bank of a little stream that coursed noisily through a narrow canyon, swollen to its limit with the rushing and melting snow as the only sign of the winter just past. Young willow bushes dotted the shoreline and clung tenaciously to the sparse ground, competing for every speck of nourishment. Bushes shared this place with small trees that were bursting with new spring growth. This location would offer the mare ideal cover from predators and protection from the harsh, biting cold that had not yet given up its wintery grip on the land. She checked carefully for danger, using her acute senses of hearing and smell to survey her surroundings. She usually felt safe in a vast expanse of land with a broad view where she could see and hear impending danger early enough to retreat. Here in the close confines of the underbrush, she was hidden from view but had to be intensely alert to her surroundings. When she sensed she was safe, she chose a secluded thicket of bushes and sank heavily down on the ground.[2]

In the clear morning air, hidden by the overhanging branches, it was here that she gave birth to a strong, healthy colt whom we shall call Darius[3]. Because he was born a wild mustang, he was also called *Tasunka* by an ancient legend of the Lakota Sioux.[4]

---

[2] If a pregnant mare feels ill at ease or in any danger, she can postpone the birth by several hours. Most mares will give birth to their foals alone at night in a secluded spot where they feel less vulnerable and so can lie down for the birth.

[3] The name Darius comes from a Bedouin legend and a famous ancient Persian king, Darius I, whose name also graces a particular type of vertical wind turbine.

[4] The Lakota are a Native American tribe. Also known as the Teton Sioux, they are one of the three prominent subcultures of the Sioux people.

Re: Tasunka: A Lakota Horse Legend by Donald F. Montileaux

The mare got up quickly to her feet and sniffed the new foal thoroughly, memorizing his scent. It would be critical to his survival that she recognize him apart from the others in the herd. She licked his wet coat roughly but tenderly with her smooth tongue, getting a sense of him. He was small with a soft, sandy-colored coat accented by a dark stripe down his back and striking, slender black legs with a black brush of mane and tail, quite unlike his darker bay mother.

~

Darius wobbled helplessly under his mother's intense grooming at first, but as his senses sharpened, he felt the strong urge to rise to his feet. He tried several times but always collapsed in a heap. He tried again, and after several futile attempts, he managed to get up

on all four spindly legs. Unable or hesitant to move, he wobbled, wavered, and fell once again. Both determined and undaunted, he caught his breath and tried again. He was finally able to stand, and after a moment, he ventured to move his legs. His mother nickered softly to him, offering encouragement, but did not help him. He would have to learn to move his legs all by himself.[5]

---

[5] It is imperative that new foals learn their mothers' sound, imprint her scent on their brain, and remember her shape, separating it from all other horses, as this is vital to their early survival when they are the most vulnerable.

The young foal might be small of stature when grown, standing at only a little over fourteen hands[6], but he would be swift and run like the wind, outdistancing any of the other horses that would challenge him. The gift of speed would prove to his advantage when larger colts began to pick on him as they vied for leadership status.

When Darius felt steady enough, he wobbled over to his mother's flank. He would now instinctively follow her wherever she went. The scent of his mother's warm, sweet milk was enticing.[7] Nosing under her warm flank, he found the source of her milk and filled his belly with his first meal. Warm and satisfied,

---

[6] Hand: A horse's size or height is measured in "hands." The hand is a measurement of length standardized to 4 inches (10.2 cm). It is used to measure the height of horses in many English-speaking countries. It was originally based on the breadth of a human hand.

[7] This first milk is essential to a young colt as it contains colostrum, with all the nutrients and antibodies needed to protect him and give him a good start in life.

he became sleepy and very, very tired. Sensing this and because the thicket of trees was a secure place, the mare was content to let him rest. She, too, was exhausted and slept fitfully on her feet, standing protectively over him. Her ears would flick back and forth, sensitive to any new noise that she did not recognize. After a short rest, the new baby awoke refreshed and with each drink of the mare's milk and short naps, the little foal gained strength and a greater awareness of his surroundings.

Once the mare felt confident enough to return to her family with her new foal at her side, she headed to the stream for a drink of water and then, turned resolutely toward the ridge and the mesa above. The young foal had no choice but to follow her. Haltingly at first, he stumbled but eventually found his footing and was able to stay up on his legs close to his mother's side, where he felt the most secure.

The return trek to the herd took a lot longer. The newborn tired quickly and needed to rest frequently to regain his strength. They slowly made their way up the incline as the going was hard, steep, and not secure underfoot. But the little foal persevered with each of his mother's soft nickers as she patiently waited for him to catch up.

As they came over the top of the rise, the mare let out a clear whinny, hoping to locate the other horses. She listened intently; ears attuned to any sound. Finally, hearing the stallion's return whinny loud and clear, she headed in his direction, occasionally calling to him in return.

It took a while to reach the band with her foal. Darius could not move faster than a walk; trotting, cantering, and a full gallop would come later. As they approached the herd, the mares stopped their grazing and raised their heads. Their ears had sensed the mare's movement on the horizon, but as she came closer, they looked inquisitively in her direction. They were not immediately sure who she was, especially with another tagging along beside her, but they were intently curious. Some snorted and blew through their nostrils with alarm; others stomped their forefeet with uncertainty and false bravado. The stallion was as aware of the mare's return as he had been of her departure.[8] He called to her again, and she answered. The other mares then recognizing her whinny, acknowledged her presence.

To keep her baby at a distance from the others would not be an easy task as the new

---

[8] For the mares, it was not part of their daily routine to keep track of individuals. They had their favorites with whom they would stay close, but otherwise their awareness was of the family group. The stallion, on the other hand, knew the mares as individuals and kept track of each of them.

foal was a curiosity to all of them, generating a great deal of interest. The mare would need to keep her baby close by her side so he would not be confused by the other horses' scent and appearances during this critical, definitive time as he bonded with his mother. Mothers had to be continually vigilant, especially when her young foal would drop to the grass and fall immediately asleep. Then she would stand guard over him, ever alert to danger. Hers was the first birth that spring, followed shortly by the other mares who had their own young to watch over.

Spring foaling was a busy time for the stallion. As a conscientious leader, he devoted his time to watching over his mares and their offspring. His alertness heightened with each new arrival. The small family group now consisted of the stallion, five mares, and five new arrivals.

Darius' older sister, born several years before, still stayed close to her mother. She had given birth to a little filly. It was to this little foal that Darius made his first furtive attempts at approaching the other horses. She was small like him but very shy and tended to stay beneath

her mother's tail whenever another horse came near her. After Darius made several inquisitive advances, the little filly, realizing he was not a threat, allowed him to approach her. However, if something made her feel unsure, she would turn and scamper back to her mother. This sudden motion would cause a chain reaction in Darius, and he, too, would react by running back to his mother. This back-and-forth dance went on for several days until finally Darius and the filly developed a tentative bond. They would synchronize their movements, eating and sleeping at the same time.

~

Darius' grandmother was the lead mare, whose advanced years had afforded her much wisdom. She guided the herd along famil- iar, well-worn paths to safe grazing areas.

She knew when to travel to the hills, where it was cooler in summer, and how to avoid hordes of flies. She knew where to find shelter during the winter from brutal blizzards on the western plains. The old mare's wisdom led the small band for many seasons through the reign of several stallions. It was now the black stallion's turn to raise his get[9] and live among the mares. Darius was born to the herd's top lineage as the stallion's favorite mare and the lead mare's grandson. This gave him many advantages. Along with his mother, he would not have to compete for the greenest and most succulent grasses. He also enjoyed immediate protection from the stallion as a lead colt—a position he instinctively had to defend from a larger piebald colt.[10]

---

[9] Get: An animal's offspring.

[10] Piebald: spotted or patched, especially black and white such as a piebald horse. In North America, the term for this coloring pattern is also called pinto.

Darius had the good fortune to be born to a strong, intelligent sire and dam[11] which gave him the resilience and instinct to survive significant challenges and hardships. He was a mustang,[12] small and strong, an animal capable of living on the often-difficult Great Plains. He was America's horse, with an inherited toughness honed by centuries of survival, and Darius would have to call upon these resources many times in his young life.

~

---

[11] Sire: a stallion who has offspring; dam: a mare who has given birth to a foal.

[12] Mustang: a small, hardy wild horse of the North America plains, whose ancestors were Spanish barbs, descended from Arabian horses brought to America by the Spanish explorers in the 1500s. These horses had been turned loose to run wild after the Spanish conquest of the New World.

CHAPTER TWO

EARLY YEARS

As the bright, clear days of early spring slowly but steadily gave way to warmer days, a complement of five foals had arrived. Besides Darius, there were two fillies, a large, husky piebald colt, and a smaller, rather shy chestnut colt. The youngsters were all healthy, full of vigor, and endowed with an insatiable energy and curiosity. Their days consisted of filling their bellies with mother's milk, taking short naps, and then bursting forth with renewed energy, testing their legs to see how fast they could run. Galloping and circling the herd, they ran around an imaginary obstacle course that changed from minute to minute. Each foal would slide to a stop, turn, and tear off again in another direction. All this exuberance would help build strong muscles and bones and develop the agility they would need in the coming months and years.

Life was easy in these early months. Darius loved to lie down and stretch out full length with his nose buried deep in the sweet-scented grasses of blue flag, cordgrass, milkweed, and sedge. The hot sun penetrated his body with a warmth and security that Darius loved. Slowly and blissfully, he would surrender to a deep sleep lulled by the comforting sounds of his mother chewing the grasses nearby.

The little band stayed on the plateau as the grass was plentiful and sweet. Predators were nowhere to be seen. The days were long, lazy, and pleasantly warm. Frequently a sudden burst of a warm breeze drove the ever-present flies away. Occasionally, the pastoral tranquility of this scene, much enjoyed by the horses, was shattered as a thunderstorm rose quickly over the horizon, darkening the landscape. A torrent of rain and a loud crack of thunder were all the excuse the colts needed to take off at full gallop, running circles around their dams and the fillies. Because of his speed, Darius could outdistance the other colts and enjoyed doing so every time.

The large piebald colt was always challenging Darius and tried to intimidate him at every opportunity. Sensing play, Darius would tempt the piebald colt by getting just close enough to him to cause the colt to react. The piebald took the bait every time and the chase began. Darius stayed just enough ahead of the other colt to keep taunting him. Never winded and never at a loss for speed, Dar- ius repeatedly played this game with the pie-bald colt, who never seemed to catch onto the fact that it was all in fun. Sometimes Darius walked close enough among the others, swishing his brush of a tail, so that the piebald would take chase once again. It was a good game for Darius and one that entertained him during those early months.

As spring slipped silently into the oppressive heat of summer, the horses began to work their way toward the foothills at the north end of the plateau. One clear, chilly morning, Darius' grandmother started toward a familiar, well-worn path that wound up the mountainside. She had followed this path many times in the past. It was a narrow slip of ground winding its way amongst sage and thistle, a path almost invisible to the untrained eye. The rest of the herd took her

cue and followed. The stallion brought up the rear to protect their flank as well as to see what was behind them.

~

The sun rose hot and steady as it climbed to its zenith in the sky. Before long, the herd stopped to rest in the shade of some pinyon pines. The air up here was cooler, and the biting flies were almost absent. As they climbed higher, the horses were thirsty but had to wait until the mare led them to a small trickling mountain stream higher up amongst the rocky crags. By late afternoon, they had reached the sweet mountain meadows grazed by the mountain goats and Dall sheep that lived there.

Never having seen these smaller creatures before, Darius reacted by snorting and dashing to his mother's side. But he was curious about them and raised his head high with ears cocked forward. He snorted several times, stamped hard with his forefoot to try to get them to move. His mother did not respond to his cue. She had seen the goats and sheep many times before and grazed calmly, ignoring her son's antics as she searched for the sweetest new shoots of mountain grass. Since his mother remained calm around the goats and sheep, Darius soon realized that the animals were not a threat. Instead, he grew to enjoy having them around. They were an interesting diversion for the young horse.

Here in the high mountains, the small band lived out the seemingly endless days of summer. Life was good, simple, and comfortable this time of year and luckily devoid of predators such as bears, cougars, or coyotes on this side of the mountain. Nourished by the sweet mountain grasses, the colts grew quickly into their long legs. The two fillies bonded and spent most of their time together. Darius still taunted the piebald colt, although he could not run as fast over the uneven ground and rocky hillside as he had down on the plains. But he still took delight in baiting the larger colt.

The days grew shorter, and the temperature dropped, and the mares began to wend their way down the mountainside to avoid the harsh winters on the mountain range. As they descended, a sudden flurry of snow-flakes blew up and swirled about them, obscuring their vision. The young colts and fillies—filled with renewed energy in the freezing air—responded by bucking and rearing and kicking up their heels. As suddenly as the snow squall had arrived, it disappeared just as quickly, leaving behind a clear, cold, sunny day. The trip down the mountain now seemed shorter as the youngsters were more robust and had more stamina.

Autumn saw the aspen trees change their leaves from soft green to a bright golden yellow, whereas the pines and spruce stood out in a dark, rich green contrast. The air grew colder, and the light faded from the days. The nights were electric, littered with millions of stars overhead, and bitterly cold. The horses adjusted to this change in the temperature by growing warm winter coats. The new growth looked like soft velvet, and as the days shortened, their coats grew longer, with a layer of soft, fluffy down, topped with long, hollow hairs that would catch and conserve the heat from their bodies. In these new coats, they were most comfortable. They had eaten well on the mountain and now had an extra layer of fat to see them through the lean days ahead. The colder temperatures gave the youngsters a renewed energy source as they ran, galloped, bucked, and reared to their hearts' content. Their dams by now had weaned them of milk by walking away when a youngster came to nurse. The young ones became discouraged and, mimicking their mothers, now fed on grass full time. The mares had tired of all the rambunctious play and became so short-tempered, they would pin their ears back and bare their teeth at the young ones. They knew the coming months would be lean with food in short supply. It was no time for fun.

CHAPTER THREE

THE FIRST WINTER

The first real snowstorm of the season blew down from the mountains and onto the plateau and plains below, blanketing everything. Darius awoke covered entirely in the white stuff. He sniffed it, blew at it, and it flew all over the place. The snow startled Darius. He jumped to his feet, galloped around in circles, and kicked up his heels shaking the snow from his coat. The other colts joined in, and a wonderful game took shape as they frolicked endlessly, enjoying the snow flying everywhere about them. However, it was not long before the new winter snow's novelty wore off, and it continued to fall heavily throughout the day.

It soon became evident to the youngsters that they would have to paw through the snow to reach the dry grass underneath. The extra effort this required stole much of their energy, and they quickly tired. It seemed as if in a split second, the carefree life they had always known was gone. It was bitter cold most of the time; the sun was at such a low angle that it did not warm them during the day, and the nights were clear, sprinkled with millions of stars, densely cold, tenaciously forming ice crystals on their nostrils, chin, and ears. A shake of the head failed to dislodge the ice. Frustrated, they would paw the ground vigorously without relief. Sometimes a full moon rose slowly but steadily above the horizon, lighting up the darkness as it showered a thin, cold light over the land. But moonlight did nothing to raise the temperature, even if it allowed better vision, especially with the bright white snow covering.

This winter was more severe than most. It took its toll on the plains' creatures when the small band lost one of its mares. Weakened from searching for food, she could no longer stand for long periods. Eventually, she lost interest in eating. On one clear night, she wandered off and was discovered the next morning as if asleep, covered lightly with snow. The herd moved on, unable to expend energy waiting for her to get up and travel with them.

~

One especially brutal storm raged on for days. The lead mare searched for cover and soon found a small grove of spruce trees that would offer much-needed protection from the biting wind and heavy snow swirling and howling around them. The herd gathered in amongst the tall spruce trees by forming a circle, with their tails exposed to the elements. The youngsters were in the center of the ring and thereby afforded more protection from the wind and cold. Here they waited out the storm, neither eating nor drinking. Their extra stores of fat would likely see them through this difficult time.

As the storm weakened, sunlight slipped through the heavy clouds and warmed the day. It remained unseasonably warm for the next week, melting the deep snow and giving the horses a welcomed break from the harsh winter, but it again turned bitter cold and remained so until spring.

CHAPTER FOUR

YEARLINGS

With winter finally over, the vitality of spring was a welcome sight. Heavy winter coats were now itchy, and the horses spent a great deal of time rolling on the ground to scratch and discard the old hair, giving way to a lighter spring and summer coat. Darius' mother again wandered away from the herd only to return with a brand-new foal. Darius was perplexed and confused with the arrival of the newcomer. His mother ignored his curious advances by pinning her ears back, lowering her head in a threatening posture as she positioned herself between her new foal and her son. He suffered a strange feeling of separation and confused jealousy but soon became distracted by the other yearling colts. The mare's rebuff turned out to be the final separation for mother and son, as was the natural way of things.

Darius now spent most of his time amongst the other yearlings, who fell into the rhythm of the group, eating, resting, and moving with them. Before, they had moved alongside their dams, but this was different; now they were in tune with the whole herd. They still cavorted and galloped about, although their play was much less exuberant than last year.

Spring again held its promise of warm, sunny days, fresh grass, new life, and flies. When the flies appeared in great number, the old mare again turned the herd to the mountain hillside. The trek was more familiar for Darius and the other youngsters. Summer passed uneventfully, and as the days shortened and the air cooled, the mare led them an alternate way down to the valley floor. There they would spend the winter amongst the pinyon pines and scrub brush.

Winter arrived in stages and grew more intense. The horses fed closer to the tall pines and Douglas fir trees scattered along the side of a nearby river, affording them protection within the trees during more serious storms. Darius' second winter was easier for him. It appeared that he learned lessons from last year on how to survive during these strenuous months, or maybe the winter was milder with fewer storms. Either way, spring seemed to come more quickly so that all the horses welcomed the retreat of winter's grip on the prairie.

Darius' mother wandered away and then returned to the band with a small filly, and the other mares, in turn, returned with their new foals as well. The herd was growing and moved more frequently as there were many more mouths to feed. Darius was now three years old, quite impressed with himself. The stallion, however, was about to chase the three-year-old colts from the herd. The two fillies would probably stay with their mothers for the time being. More than likely, another stallion, perhaps one of the bachelor stallions roaming freely over the prairie, would kidnap them. Darius would have joined one of these bachelor bands had circumstances not come into play.

CHAPTER FIVE

LOSS OF A LEADER

One bright, clear afternoon, the band was traveling down from a mesa[13] toward an interstate highway. The mares and young had crossed the road and gone down the embankment on the far side, but the stallion hesitated, looking around to make sure all was safe. Just as he started to cross, a large, long-haul tractor-trailer came speeding toward him.

Jerry McMahon had been a truck driver for over twenty years and had traveled this

---

[13] An isolated flat-topped hill with steep sides.

route many times. He was single, forty-five years old, shorter and wirier than most men his age, a man who loved the open road and the freedom it offered him. Jerry loved animals, especially horses. As a young man, because of his size, he thought about becoming a jockey. When this did not happen, he found an advertisement about truck driving and signed up on the dotted line. He was considered a happy person, full of optimism, by all who knew him. Whenever a joyously good mood overtook him, he would sing along with the country music radio station that played all his favorite tunes. The radio kept him company on long trips. Sometimes on an unusually straight stretch of highway, he would get lost in a song, feeling its vibes as it carried him along. He banged on the steering wheel in rhythm with the steady beat of the music. Today he was running a bit behind schedule and was trying to make up some time. Jerry took great pride in making his deliveries on time since he drove a "reifer" or refrigerator truck.

Heading west directly into the afternoon sun, he saw the mares cross the road. Whenever Jerry saw the wild horses, he marveled at their beauty, their majesty, and the incredible sense of their wildness. He did not see the dark stallion initally, and when he did see the stallion on the road, applying his brakes did little to slow him down. The truck sideswiped the stallion as he crossed to the bank on the far side of the highway. Jerry continued to apply the brakes, but it still took more than 500 yards for the heavy truck to come to a complete stop. Jerry jumped down from the cab and ran back to where the injured horse lay.

The stallion was still breathing, but his sides were heaving, and his eyes stared blankly into space. Blood slowly trickled from his mouth and nose. Sensing the stallion was mortally wounded, Jerry raced back to his truck, grabbed his pistol from beneath his bunk, and returned to the accident. He loved the wild horses and hated to shoot such a beautiful animal, but he could see the horse was in shock and suffering. The stallion made no effort to get to his feet when Jerry approached, which told Jerry how serious the situation was. Therefore, he took a deep breath and put a bullet through the black horse's beautiful, broad head without any further hesitation immediately putting an end to his suffering. Taking one last look at the mares with their young as they milled around below the embankment about a quarter of a mile away, still waiting for their stallion to join them, Jerry slowly walked back to his truck. There he placed a call to the state police to report the accident and the grand stallion's death. Putting his vehicle in gear, he pulled back onto the highway, not taking the time to see if there was any damage to his truck or the trailer he was hauling. It would be a long time before Jerry would be able to forget this day.

With the rest of the herd, Darius waited aimlessly on the north side of the highway for their stallion. The lead mare kept looking back over the far side of the road to see if the stallion would appear. She called out with a clear whinny several times, waited for an answer, but none came. Sensing something was wrong, she galloped northward away from the highway for about a mile, followed by the other horses. Again, she anxiously looked to see if the stallion was coming to join them. Without a stallion, the band lost the cohesiveness that cemented the bond that held the family group together. Stallions afford the herd protection from all the dangers that might befall them. Without this leadership, the mares would be aimlessly traveling north across the plains—fair game for a take-over by a wandering bachelor stallion or, worse, a pack of coyotes who could weed out the band's young and weaker members.

CHAPTER SIX

COUGAR ATTACK

One mid-morning, they came upon a small canyon, and although they were hesitant about the narrow canyon walls, the horses knew they had to make their way through to the other side. High up on the rock ledge overlooking the path below, there rested a young female cougar,[14] outstretched and warming herself on the rocks in the morning sun. She heard the horses approaching long before she saw them. The small band was a windfall for

---

[14] Cougar: This powerful predator roams the Americas, where it is also known as a panther, puma, mountain lion, and catamount.

her. She was not hungry, but she could not pass up the chance for a meal when the opportunity presented itself. The horses below had not seen her nor caught her scent high above. As a young lioness, she was still perfecting the techniques that would ensure her survival. Now fully awake, instinct took over. She crouched low on the ledge, making herself almost invisible against the skyline. As each horse passed below, she assessed her chances of a kill. By the time Darius came through the pass, she had decided she must make her move or lose out altogether. She leaped into the air and landed squarely on Darius' back with her forepaw claws dug deep in his shoulder muscles.

~

Immediately Darius sprang into the air and reared high on his hind legs. He came down hard, and as he did, he kicked out with his hindquarters, twisted, and reared up again. Filled with an intense terror, he reared and bucked, twisting his body trying to rid himself of the menace that clung to his back. He did this several times, and each time he quickened his movements, squealing loudly. The powerful force of his actions took the young lioness by surprise, and she lost her grip on him. She was thrown savagely against the rock wall as Darius reared high, pawed the air with his forelegs, and pirouetted, with his whole body twisting in midair. The cat crashed into the canyon wall, but Darius still felt her presence on his back, causing him to run and buck for over a quarter mile. Terror quickly electrified the rest of the herd, and they, too, took off at a gallop across the plains. Even though they were not aware of the threat, they were aware of Darius' reaction, and they sensed their survival depended on escaping and galloping after him.

They traveled like this for the rest of the day, sometimes at a trot, sometimes at a canter, but without stopping to rest. This only served to tire the youngsters, who had no choice but to follow. It was not until dusk that they ultimately stopped to eat and catch their wind. A crescent moon rose high above the plains, giving a soft glow to the herd and better vision to the night. They relaxed their exhausted bodies while the youngsters slept deeply, confident they were safe with their dams standing guard. Without a stallion to watch over them, each horse silently stood lookout. It was a fitful night for Darius. The initial shock caused by the cougar attack had worn off, but there were long gashes in his shoulder where the cat's claws had grabbed him. As he had thrashed and turned, trying to rid himself of her weight, she dug deeper into his muscles to stay on his back. What bleeding there was had now dried up, but his muscles began to ache. He milled around stiffly, almost continuously, and ate fitfully.

The following day again broke clear and cold. The herd made their way to a small pond where a group of pronghorn antelope was drinking their fill. The horses soon followed, and Darius waded directly into the pond up to his shoulders. The cold water felt good, cooled the hot muscles, and helped smooth out the soreness. Within a short time, his back and shoulders felt somewhat better. He clambered out of the water and shook himself vigorously. Once the horses had quenched their thirst, they wandered far across the plains for the rest of the day and throughout most of the night. The next morning, they were close to foothills lined with digger pines, trees that preferred watery roots. The grass was lush, tasty, and abundant, and the cool air helped refresh them. Some of the colts even mustered enough energy to run and buck amongst the adults. Darius' muscles were still quite sore and stiff, but each day showed improvement. The constant movement saved him from having a frozen shoulder.[15] He was young and

---

[15] Frozen shoulder: A condition affecting the shoulder, making it painful and stiff with loss of mobility.

healthy, and his recovery was relatively quick. Although he was scarred where the cougar had clawed him, mentally recovering from the cougar attack would take much longer. Horses do not forget, nor do they lose their memories.

CHAPTER SEVEN

SEPARATION

The small herd stayed amongst the foothills' digger pines and lowlands for the rest of the warm months. The grass was good, and there were no predators except for the occasional coyote who trotted by, eyeing the horses with casual interest but then moving on. These coyotes were not an immediate threat now that the foals born this year had lived past their early critical months. However, staying in one place for an extended time left the horses open to being spotted by horse hunters who frequented this area.

So it was that two young fellas, Jake Streeter and Tom Connelly, went out riding for the day after finishing their morning chores. They were inseparable, having grown up together, and now were in their late teens. They were known to be very rambunctious, much to the consternation of their single mothers. Jake was a few months older than Tom. Neither boy had been what you might call troublemakers; they were just full of the same type of youthful exuberance exhibited by the young colts. If asked to comment on the teenagers, townsfolk might shake their heads and say, *"Ya know how it is. Boys will be boys,"* reminiscing on their own younger days. Jake and Tom had seen the little band of horses in the distance on several earlier occasions. They thought today might be a good day to chase the horses, let off a bit of steam, and have some fun in the process.

Darius was the first to spot them on the far horizon. As he lifted his head, they appeared to him as horses with something strange on their backs. He snorted and blew through his nostrils, huffing loudly, trying to make sense of what he saw. Hearing him, the other horses stopped their grazing and looked in the same direction that had caused Darius' alarm. With heads held high, they trotted around in circles, stood still, and sniffed the air. Perplexed, they stared at the strange horses as they drew closer. A downwind breeze carried a scent that did not smell right. Because they did not understand these "horses," their instinct told them to flee. Darius and the other colts took off across the open country at a full gallop. The mares and young quickly followed. When Jake and Tom saw the horses running off, they began to whoop and holler, spurring their horses to follow. The more noise they made, the faster the wild horses ran, making it more fun for the boys.

Before long, the horses turned and galloped off in the opposite direction. Darius did not look back but ran as fast as he could with the chestnut colt close behind him. The rest of the herd followed. When they came upon a small rocky knoll, Darius and the chestnut veered off in one direction and the rest of the herd in another. Jake and Tom saw the two colts break off but took off after the larger group.

Darius and his companion ran for about half a mile before they slowed down to a trot when they realized that the dreaded creatures were not chasing them anymore. Finally stopping, out of breath with their flanks heaving, they noticed the rest of the herd and their pursuers were nowhere to be seen. They stood very still, searching for any sign of their companions, and listening by flicking their ears back and forth like radar, hoping to catch a familiar sound. It was deadly quiet, with not even a whisper of a breeze. No horses came into sight. Evening fell, and the two colts huddled close together, lost and alone without their family, with whom they had spent their entire young lives.

CHAPTER EIGHT

THE OLD STALLION

Over the next several days, the two colts wandered without purpose, grazed sporadically, slept fitfully, and rested little. They would occasionally raise their heads and whinny, trying to get a response. Typically, they would have remained silent, communicating mostly with body language to avoid attracting predators, but Darius and the chestnut colt were beyond caution. They were desperately searching for their family.

A few weeks went by, and they came upon a rocky outcropping. Looking for the sparse grass that grew between the crags, the chestnut colt happened to take a wrong step on the uneven ground and twisted the fetlock on his right foreleg.[16] He squealed in pain and almost stumbled to the ground but was able to catch his fall. Tentatively, he took a few steps on three legs and found that he could slowly limp along after Darius. It was in this fashion that they wandered about with no direct purpose or path in mind. The days were hot, devoid of any cooling breeze. The only relief came with the cold nights typical of the desert. Unfortunately, the colt was not getting better and became steadily weaker. As his stamina diminished, he stopped eating. Darius sensed this change in his companion but could not understand why he was different. He could do nothing but stay with the colt for company and security.

---

[16] Foreleg: Either of the front legs of a four-footed animal.

It was not long before a lone coyote began to follow them, staying at a distance but never out of sight. This was of no concern to Darius, but the chestnut colt was starting to lose his acute sense of awareness. A day came when the colt lay down on the ground, never to get up again. Wanting to move on, Darius nickered encouragement, urging him to rise and follow, but the colt could not get to his feet. Eventually, Darius moved some distance from his companion. The coyote, sensing an opportunity, then circled and came closer to the chestnut colt. He sniffed the air to assess the condition of the wounded animal. Feeling confident, he took a quick nip at the colt's flank. When the colt barely moved, the coyote moved in closer. It was time for the injured colt, so the end came quickly for him. Darius, realizing that something had changed in his companion, trotted off.

Darius was now utterly alone. And he was terrified.

Security comes in numbers for horses, with many watchful and alert ears and eyes. Now Darius had no one to warn him of unseen dangers. As a wild horse, he was born with the many senses needed for survival, but he did not know this. The only instinct he felt now was panic at being alone without other horses for companionship.

After leaving the chestnut colt, he galloped away, trying to escape the fear that consumed him. When his lungs hurt and his sides heaved, he stopped running. The silence was deafening. There were no other creatures around; no flies, birds, nothing. A gentle breeze blew up and rustled the grass, but that was all. Overwhelmed by the silence and consumed with panic, Darius fell silent himself. He lost his sense of hunger and wandered for days eating little, changing gaits between trotting and cantering, always with his head held high as he surveyed the horizon, searching for his herd. Several times, he stopped for a long drink in a stream or pond. He could not survive without water.

Darius spent his days and nights looking for companions. Without sufficient food, his ribs began to show. His mane was matted, and his tail became tangled. He was starting to look gaunt. Fear and loneliness were dictating his existence. Three weeks had passed; the air was getting colder and the days shorter.

It was about that time that he came upon an older stallion with several mares and young. At first, he was not sure what he was seeing, but then he called out, not as a challenge, but with a call born of loneliness and desperation. He trotted toward the small group, paused, anxiously awaiting a signal from the stallion, then trotted forward again—his head held high, ears erect. Seeing Darius, the stallion raised his craggy head but did not move as he waited for Darius to come closer, observing him as he approached. The old stallion realized the colt was young and did not try to stop him.

Not knowing what to expect and unsure of these strangers, Darius stayed about fifty yards away. He immediately felt the fear slip from his mind and body.

When the others ignored him, Darius sensed his hunger slowly returning and began to graze nearby. Darius thus spent the remainder of the fall and winter season safe in the company of the old stallion and his mares. He never mingled amongst them. His senses told him to stay a respectful distance apart, and so it was that the old stallion accepted Darius and allowed him to stay near the group.

CHAPTER NINE

HERD LEADER

Darius stayed with the old stallion and his little band of mares through the following year. He was content in their company and he added an extra pair of eyes and ears to look for danger. Later the following spring, the old stallion visibly slowed down. Darius instinctively saw an opportunity to challenge the older one's leadership. He started by moving closer to the mares. It was a gentle threat that the stallion ignored, but when Darius began to show more interest

in the mares, the stallion approached him with his head low, ears pinned back. Darius understood this threat and trotted over to the stallion, accepting his challenge. The two stallions danced around each other, assessing the other's strength and agility. The old stallion made the first move by charging Darius, who pivoted out of the way, turned, and galloped headlong into the stallion's side with teeth bared and ears back. The move knocked the old stallion sideways, but he did not lose his balance. He retaliated by rearing on his hind legs and pawing the air with his forelegs, mouth open with teeth bared. Darius swerved and landed a hard kick with his back legs into the stallion's head. The stallion stumbled, faltered, but again, did not fall. Noticing an advantage, Darius swerved and slammed into the stallion, which caused the stallion to lose his balance and fall to the ground. Darius kicked him, and when the stallion found the opportunity to get to his feet, he did not rechallenge the younger horse.

~

Sensing the fight was over, Darius watched the older stallion trot off. Shaking his head and the dust from his body, he went to claim the mares. At first, they ignored him but came to accept that he was now their new leader. The old stallion stayed in the area for several days but eventually disappeared altogether.

Darius was now responsible for three mares and two colts and instinctively felt a bond to protect the little band against all odds. His early life had served him well, and he turned out to be a good leader. Over the next several years, he sired several fillies and a couple of colts. He was now a mature six-year-old mustang, still on the small side, but well filled out with strong legs and clear, intelligent eyes, leading the life to which he was born.

He proved to be a successful stallion and was fortunate not to have been spotted by the horse hunters. If they had spotted him, they ignored him; it was not worth the expense and effort to corral such a small band.

CHAPTER TEN

CAPTURE

Days flowed smoothly for Darius, consisting of finding good grassland, protecting the band from the cold and freezing winters, and watching out for predators and the man-horses. The young colts were encouraged to find life on their own once they matured. His herd grew and decreased as time passed. Life settled into a regular pattern: spring on the grassland, summers in the foothills, and the winters protected amongst the sugar pines and Douglas fir.

However, life does have a way of changing. One day the band was located by a spotter helicopter, which had the advantage over riders and vehicles to be able to cover a lot more territory in a short time. Radioing their location to the horse riders on the ground, the pilot then circled and zeroed in on the horses, flying low enough to scare them into moving. Darius heard the terrifying sound long before he saw the helicopter. He snorted and immediately began to circle the mares and foals. They took off away from the aircraft as they tried to outrun the flying monster—traveling in precisely the direction the pilot wanted them to go. He was an expert in herding horses from the air and had a great deal of territory to cover before they would meet up with the roundup team. The horses were terrified. They could do nothing but

gallop away from the loud noise as fast as possible. They felt a lack of air in their lungs, and their muscles hurt from the lack of oxygen. The younger foals were more stressed than the older horses as they tried to keep up. The pilot was either unaware of their exhaustion or did not care; his job was to get the horses to a predetermined meeting point as quickly as possible where the roundup team would take over. Several of the colts stumbled. One colt sprained his leg and fell behind. As the roundup riders came into view, the helicopter rose and banked off in the opposite direction, leaving the exhausted band to the man-horses.

The roundup team leader saw that the animals were exhausted and silently swore at the pilot for pushing them so hard; he did not want to lose any of these horses as he was paid for each one captured. He yelled to his men to hold the animals, allowing them to slow down and rest. With heaving sides, exhausted, the herd stopped, unconcerned about the man-horses on the ridge. When the leader felt the horses had rested some, he gave the signal to begin herding them toward the capture point.

At a slow trot, the herd moved off, directed by the men. After a few minutes, they came upon a wall constructed of sheets of burlap. Perceiving it to be a solid barrier, they trotted alongside it. Presently another burlap wall appeared on the opposite side. The wild horses continued down the lane it created, thinking it was a way out. The route gradually narrowed into a chute until the horses realized they were in a large corral and at a dead end with the man-horses behind them. Darius whirled around to make his escape as the gate slammed shut. They were trapped inside!

∽

Darius turned to face his tormentors. The rest of the horses followed him, and almost immediately, the corral filled with dust. So accustomed to clean, fresh air, they choked on the thick air stirred up as they ran around in circles. In the confusion and confinement that followed, each horse felt a terror entirely unknown before. They could not see; their thirst was extreme; and they keenly felt the lack of freedom as they tried to run away from that which they feared. The men stood quietly, waiting for the new arrivals to quiet down, as they knew they must.

A half hour passed. The horses tired of milling about the corral. With sides heaving and heads hung low, they stood still, beaten by exhaustion. Then the men began to fill two metal tubs with water even though they knew this would scare the horses into moving around the corral again. This time they did not run around for very long and settled down within a few minutes. Some of the mares cautiously approached the water tanks, sniffed them, but did not drink; the tanks reeked of the strange smell of men, full of sweat and leather and strange horses. Knowing that these horses would be inside the corral with something to quench their thirst, the men mounted up and galloped away.

Night fell with an uneasy silence among the group of mustangs. Darius approached the offered water and drank his fill. Soon the other horses approached the tanks, hesitant at first, but sensing no danger, drank as well. The cool night air gave them a renewed strength. Some of them began milling about the corral again, looking for a means of escape. There was none. The sturdy wooden logs that defined the corral boundary were over twelve feet high, much too high to jump over. Still, their renewed energy and fear compelled them to roam aimlessly about the dusty corral until morning brought a new day.

The men returned mid-morning with a truckload of hay that they threw in the corral and left again. Hunger overtook the horses, and they began to eat. The routine of being supplied with fresh water and hay continued this way for several days. The men always left the horses alone afterward. With the loss of their freedom, the herd soon settled into a daily routine. There were few disputes among the horses. After all, they knew each other and had not been thrown together with unfamiliar horses. Long ago, a hierarchy had formed where each animal knew its position in the family group and took comfort from each other's presence.

CHAPTER ELEVEN

CONFINEMENT

The horses would not have known that the men were waiting for a large stock trailer to pick up Darius and his small group and transport them to Nevada's large holding pens. Late one morning, a tractor-trailer truck appeared large and foreboding as it rattled up the dirt road toward the corral. It raised clouds of dust, screeching, and hissing its brakes as it bounced to an abrupt stop. The commotion sent the horses in a panic around the corral. The truck appeared to them to be a giant monster from which there was no escape. When the truck stopped making noise, they settled down again, staring at the large vehicle for any sign of movement. Several of the men approached the corral and erected a temporary canvas chute through which they planned to drive the horses up a ramp and onto the truck.

Herding the horses onto the trailer caused them to bunch together. Several slipped and fell. Two of these animals were young and were trampled in the noise and confusion. Once they were on the trailer, the panic was overwhelming for animals used to being wild and free, with no borders and fresh air filling their lungs. Crowded together in the trailer with metal bars, smelling of oil and grease, and lurching over the dirt roads to the main highway, each horse knowing only solid ground underfoot, continually had to shift its weight to stay upright. The horses sensed that they might not be able to get up quickly on their feet if they fell.

The hot and dusty trip took the rest of the day. When they finally arrived at the holding pens maintained by the BLM[17], a ramp was lowered, the horses charged forth, thinking they had found their freedom, only to find themselves in yet another enclosure

---

[17] BLM: The Bureau of Land Management is a U.S. Government agency charged with handling the "wild horse problem." The BLM has sought to seek common ground between the cattle ranchers using public lands who feel strongly that the horses are eating their cattle out of existence and the wild horse lovers who believe the wild horse is a public trust and has a given right to roam free on the expansive public lands in the West from which they came. Both sides have strong arguments, but the real fact is those horses caught in the middle either live out their lives milling around in holding pens, a practice that is expensive to maintain or are put in the annual horse auction where select individuals are screened for their suitability to care for a wild horse. A lot of the "adopted" horses are then sent to slaughter houses. A skeptical sterilization program is another practice used on mares, but still the numbers do not diminish to any great degree. Darius was considered for this latter group and had been singled out to be prepared for adoption.

surrounded by many other pens filled with other horses. Even though they were hot and tired, they fearfully galloped around the pen.

Dusk comes quickly to the desert, and night surrounded them in darkness, which helped settle the new arrivals. The horses in the other pens nearby were quiet, and so Darius' band became quiet as well. Fear had erased their hunger earlier in the day, but now it returned with nothing to eat or drink. Standing on three legs, resting the fourth, head lowered, the new arrivals drifted into a

fitful sleep. None of them felt safe enough to lie down, even for a moment.

The next morning came all too quickly with activity picking up around the holding pens. Men walked past, talking, calling to one another. There were a lot of new sounds and smells swirling around. The new arrivals received hay in pellet form along with fresh water. They were not used to pellets, but, curious about the hay scent, they investigated and found them easy to chew. When their hunger was satisfied and their thirst quenched, they stood watching the activity rustling around them. The sun rose high over the pens, and the dry heat rapidly sucked any remaining moisture from the air, making standing in close quarters almost insufferable.

The strange noises, smells, and activity strained the newly arrived wild horses' nerves.

They had spent their entire lives in the relative calm and quiet found on the great expanse of the plains of their birth. Any unfamiliar sound would send them rushing around in a circle, nervous and anxious. Learning to adjust to this new environment would take time.

The other horses had adjusted to their fate. The air was heavy under the hot sun as they milled around the pens. The routine never changed except for the daily arrival of food and water. Boredom was ever-present. These animals were so far removed from their birthright, they hardly looked like the wild horses roaming free on the plains. Darius and his small band now found themselves in this environment.

~

Two men came into the corral early one morning and threw a rope over Darius' head. The slap of the rope around his neck made him charge away from the men, which only served to tighten the noose around his neck, cutting off his air supply. He had no choice but to stop and stand still, terrified. With all his senses alert, he waited for their next move. The men were experienced in handling these horses and approached him carefully, walking slowly toward him with deliberate steps, not looking at him directly, speaking in soft, soothing tones. When they attempted to make him move by pulling on the rope, he again became anxious.

In horse society, anyone who can make you move your feet is more substantial and holds dominance over you. Darius wanted to stay put, moving only when *he* wanted to.

Nonetheless, the men knew how to move him by pulling him off balance so as to move his forefeet, making him move right or left to regain his balance, as they continued to move him toward the gate where two other men were patiently waiting to transport Darius to another location. They herded him into a long, narrow chute and loaded him onto a large cattle trailer with open rail sides. Darius was selected to be "broken"[18] or trained as a cutting horse. He was with other horses separated and selected for training—all strangers, but horses nonetheless, and so he felt a small measure of comfort.

Darius along with the other horses were then transferred to the Northern Nevada

---

[18] Broken: Today, a broke horse is considered a horse that can be ridden or driven. There is no need to break a horse's spirit by rough riding and handling. The terms broke, breaking in, or breaking have stuck around regardless.

Correctional Center where similarly selected inmates were chosen, and each assigned a wild horse. A tall, burly black man, Roosevelt Brown, drew Darius as his horse. Roosevelt's mother had been fond of President Franklin Delano Roosevelt and thought such an upstanding name would help her son in life. Most everyone knew him only as Roosevelt.

Roosevelt was a quiet man in his fortieth year. He did not interact much with the other prisoners, finding it easier and safer to keep to himself. Roosevelt had a sad and melancholy way about him. He was in prison for larceny,[19] a crime he committed as a teenager. Full of bravado and daring, Roosevelt had been trying to make a name for himself among the other boys in his neighborhood. He was not part of a gang as he did not have

---

[19] Larceny: Theft of personal property.

an interest in one, but short-term thievery was another matter. It was easy and quick, and the monetary rewards were immediate. Repetition, however, landed him in jail and eventually prison. Because he was not violent and followed the prison regulations, he was selected to be part of an innovative program pairing inmates with wild horses, to give each a chance for rehabilitation and reclamation.

Darius and Roosevelt were a perfect match. Darius was a willful stallion and responded well to Roosevelt's quiet manner. Roosevelt had never been around horses and knew nothing about them, but he understood this horse: Both man and horse had their freedom roughly and suddenly taken away. As a young boy, Roosevelt never thought about horses. His only connection was seeing them in the cowboy movies that he loved to watch on television after school. His mother, a nurse, was his only support. She had to work long hours to keep a roof over their heads and food on the table. She was tired most of the time and did not have much control over the boy during those hours she was at work. Now, here in prison, Roosevelt found himself responsible for a horse and a wild one at that. Each was nervous and cautious at their first meeting.

Roosevelt stood in the corral without the slightest idea of how to proceed, and if he could admit it to himself, he was a bit afraid of the wild animal in front of him. Roosevelt barely moved but watched the horse as it ran in circles around the pen. When Darius realized the man was not coming after him, he stopped and stood watching the man, curious. He sniffed the air, trying to get a better feel for the situation. The man still did not move toward the horse. Darius was perplexed; this behavior was unfamiliar to him. He moved closer to the man, but the man stayed still. Although this tactic seemed to be working with Darius, Roosevelt was unaware of his effect on this horse. Carefully they studied each other and began to take the other's measure. When the training hour was up, Roosevelt turned and quietly left the corral, hoping the horse would not charge him when he turned his back. Darius just stood watching him.

This ritual was repeated over the next several days. Roosevelt made no effort to place a halter or a lead rope on Darius. Many of the other inmates had already gotten halters on their horses; some horses were aggressive and would attack their trainers and then back off, fearful of the men. Darius instead watched Roosevelt, expectant of a next move.

It was late one afternoon when Roosevelt started walking toward Darius. He knew instinctively not to look at him, but rather to just as quietly as possible move closer. Darius, seeing his approach, took off around the corral away from Roosevelt. Roosevelt quietly walked after him. Finally, Darius slowed down to a jerky trot, eventually whirled around, and looked at the man. When Darius stopped, Roosevelt stopped. This routine continued for a couple of days. Slowly Darius accepted Roosevelt's presence and began to look forward to his arrival as the loneliness of being separated from his fellow horses was beginning to take a toll on him. Roosevelt had befriended one of the chefs in the kitchen and one day offered Darius a carrot. Darius was a bit hesitant as he sniffed at the carrot and gently took it into his mouth. Chewing and shaking his head up and down several times, he decided he liked the taste and began searching for another. This amused Roosevelt, so he vowed to bring carrots every chance he could. As he fed Darius, a tentative rapport developed, and Roosevelt began calling him "Boy" for lack of a better name.

After a while, Roosevelt felt the horse trusted him enough to allow a rope to be placed on his back. Then he began rubbing him down with the rope. Darius tolerated this, so Roosevelt rubbed a halter over his neck and chest and eventually over his ears and face. Darius having begun to trust this man, it was not too difficult for Roosevelt to do this. After much fumbling and hesitation, Roosevelt finally placed the halter on Darius's head and snapped the buckle in place. Then he led him around the corral—no quick movements, no jerking, just slow and deliberate moves along with a soft voice. If

Darius hesitated, Roosevelt would stop and wait until Darius moved forward again.

As Roosevelt spent more time with his horse, it brought a change in him. He felt comfortable spending more time with the other "horse trainers" and became more outgoing. He liked comparing his time with Darius with the other inmates who had horses of their own to train. To him, this was as good as it gets in jail. The inmates had to train their horses to a halter and lead rope so they would walk calmly behind their trainer. Then the horses were taken away from their trainer and put up for adoption.

The day finally arrived that Roosevelt was dreading. Darius was considered "halter broke" and ready for separation. The little mustang, on the other hand, had no idea this was about to happen. Roosevelt said his goodbyes and gave Darius several carrots, which Darius relished. Not one for emotional outbursts, Roosevelt shed a few tears as he walked away from his horse, not knowing but fearing what the future had in store for his little "Boy."

CHAPTER TWELVE

AUCTION DAY

Darius was returned to the holding pens and placed with other horses destined for adoption. Here he stayed until Adoption Day. Dawn broke foggy that morning with men milling around, busy with a definite purpose or destination in mind. As the sun rose, the heat of the day cleared the fog. The horses in the holding pens sensed an urgency to the activity around them.

Darius and the other horses were moved to a smaller pen where they were fitted with halters and had a white number painted on their hip. Darius was number 22. The hectic bustle and activity made the horses nervous as they were divided into different pens designated for stallions, colts, mares, and broodmares before they could settle down.

On this day, Lester Bidwell and his granddaughter, Taylor, age eleven, visited the BLM auction. After several futile attempts, Lester had been accepted as a suitable candidate to adopt a mustang. His location, barn cover, pasture, and desire to adopt a horse under BLM conditions had been approved after a lengthy application. The fact that Taylor knew nothing about horses other than she loved them was not an immediate concern to the BLM. She had read all the horse stories she could find in the local library and imagined stories about fabulous wild horses. As her guardian, her grandfather tried to do anything he could for his granddaughter. Taylor had long wished for a real live horse, so he was eager to get one for her.

They arrived early on the day of the auction and wandered amongst the pens of the many horses. Taylor spotted Darius among about five other horses and was intrigued by his coloring; a dusty coat offset by his black mane and black legs with just a hint of black stripes. *"Look, Gramps, that horse has stripes!"* Her grandfather, noticing Darius's small stature, felt this horse would be a good match for his granddaughter. The fact that he was a stallion and maybe not suitable for an inexperienced young girl did not occur to him. Lester placed a bid for the young horse, and for whatever reason, he won, maybe because Darius was smaller than the other horses. Some prospective buyers might have taken him to be a pony, not suitable for their needs.

Taylor was thrilled and anxious to take Darius home. She jumped up and down, squealed, and gave her grandfather the biggest hug of her life. In turn, her grandfather was most pleased and beamed down a beautiful smile on his precious granddaughter. Lester had borrowed a secondhand two-horse trailer and a truck from his neighbor. All the paperwork was completed and signed after Lester agreed not to sell the horse for one year. They hailed one of the BLM men to assist them in loading Darius onto the trailer. Having some previous experience, Darius moved quickly onto the small trailer. He was easy to handle, thanks to the patience and dedication of his inmate friend, Roosevelt.

The trip took more than a day as Taylor and her grandfather had traveled a great distance overnight to get to the auction by early morning. Darius had been provided with a hay net but was nervous and unable to eat during the trip.

They arrived at their ranch toward evening; it was a modest, whitewashed, simple two-story house with a long porch on the south side, an outer shed, and a small unpainted barn mostly used for tractors and equipment. The barn had a long, open shed extending off the north side. Lester backed Darius out of the trailer and led him to the shed, where Taylor had placed some hay. Lester drew some clean, fresh water in a tin bucket for their little horse. As it was late, the pair left Darius and went to the house. Left by himself, Darius wandered around the shed cold and alone. The next morning, bright and early, Taylor ran out to the barn before breakfast to check on her new friend. She leaned over the railing and spoke softly to Darius. He watched her, not understanding who she was or how he found himself in this place. He missed the company of other horses, but the stillness at the farm was a welcome relief from the BLM yards' noise and confusion. Although Taylor was glad to have him with her, she was a little afraid of him and dared not enter the shed just yet. So instead, she resigned herself to just watching him. She saw to it he had his hay replenished and made sure his water bucket was full.

~

Darius spent his first day on the little ranch with Taylor spending every spare moment watching him and talking to him. She decided on "Dusty" as a suitable name for her new horse. She said the word repeatedly, hoping Darius would understand and know what his name was. Her grandfather came out later and checked to make sure the horse had plenty of hay to eat and clean water to drink.

Darius settled into a simple routine; hay
and fresh water in the morning, then left alone
during the day when Taylor was at school,
with more hay and fresh water at night. Boredom replaced loneliness early on. There was
nothing to change the routine, only a view of a
meadow beyond the barn bordered by a thin
line of trees. A few chickens would wander by
the shed, aimlessly scratching up dust
hunting for bugs and things to eat in the dirt.
Darius was no longer afraid of the grandfather
or Taylor, who had finally mustered up
enough courage to venture into the shed
in order to pet her horse and brush and curry

his coat. He looked forward to these visits. The currying and brushing helped to remove debris from his coat and gave him a well-needed scratch. The shed soon filled with manure and flies. Standing in the muck was uncomfortable for Darius. His hooves were always damp, and he was unable to get out of the mud. It tended to be dark and cold on the north side of the barn. The sun's warming rays never quite reached the inside of the shed, and the dark, dank place had a negative effect on the little horse.

Just when it felt as if things could not get much worse, Lester decided it was time for Darius to receive some training. He realized having the horse just standing around in a shed all the time was not suitable for this little animal. He knew of a man who might be willing to break Darius to a bridle and saddle so his granddaughter could ride him.

CHAPTER THIRTEEN

TRAINING

One Saturday morning, Lester Bidwell phoned Ben Clayton, a local horse trainer who fancied himself a bona fide horse whisperer. Ben was a middle-aged man, stockier than most, whose wife left him years before when he had a drinking problem. Ben overcame the drink and soon took to helping folks with their problem horses. He considered his talents to range far and wide, as he liked to say, *"There isn't a horse I can't handle".* He was curious about the horse so he went over to see what would be required to break Darius to ride.

At first glance, Ben saw a beautifully proportioned little horse with an intelligent and alert look to his eye. He knew at once this was a mustang, probably caught up on the high plains and sold at auction by the BLM to people like the Bidwell's who lacked any knowledge of horses but who wanted only the best for their little horse. Ben Clayton was not concerned about this situation. Having handled many mustangs in the past, he estimated it would not be much of a challenge. Darius was easy to halter and lead due to the care and patience of the inmate Roosevelt. Ben thought this was going to be easy money. He led Darius out of the dark, dank shed and into the sunlight.

After being cooped up for so long, Darius had the urge to jump and run and stretch his legs, but a sharp yank on the rope pulled him back. Ben demanded the mustang's attention. Every time Darius was distracted by something, Ben would jerk the lead rope and pull him back to gain his attention. He led Darius out to a small corral, and Darius followed willingly. Once in the corral, Ben released the lead rope and let Darius loose. At first, hesitant to move, not used to being off a lead line, Darius quickly realized he was free to move at will. He started to trot around the corral. It felt good to move again, and after a few half bucks, he settled down and stopped to watch Ben standing silently in the center of the ring. Sensing the horse was more curious than afraid, Ben walked up to Darius and hitched the rope to his halter. He had retrieved a saddle blanket in his left hand and began shaking it around Darius' shoulder. Darius shied from the movement at first but quickly realized the blanket would not hurt him. Ben rubbed the blanket against Darius' side, which the horse stood for. He was a bit anxious, but not enough to bolt. Ben was sensitive to the young horse. He watched Darius' eyes, how his ears moved, his head and body positions. These signals told him all he needed to know about the horse's mood. What he did not know was Darius' history.

When he thought Darius had settled down, Ben tossed the blanket over Darius's back and was startled by the horse's instant reaction. The weight of something on his back brought back a flood of memories of the cougar attack. His immediate response was to dislodge the blanket as quickly as possible. He reared up in the air, ripping the rope out of Ben's hand. Free, he bucked and reared again in the air, then galloped around the corral until he sensed the blanket was gone. Ben watched in amazement at the sudden and violent reaction. Taming this horse might not be as simple a task as he had initially thought.

However, Ben was not a man to give up easily and felt up to the challenge. He spent the next six weeks trying to place a saddle or at least a blanket on the mustang's back. It now came down to his reputation as a horse trainer, or whisperer, as he liked to think of himself. But this little horse could fool a person. He was easy to be around, trusting, and with a pleasant disposition, but he was hellbent against allowing anything to be placed on his back. Of course, Ben had no way of knowing what had caused Darius' violent behavior. He only knew that this horse was not for a young, inexperienced girl to ride, even if she could ever get on his back. Ben finally had to admit defeat to Lester Bidwell. He recommended that Lester sell the horse to someone who could use an unbroken horse or maybe send him to a meatpacking processor as the horse was not much good to anyone in his present condition. Lester thoughtfully took this advice, remembering he had signed a contract not to sell the horse for one year. It looked like they were only going to have the little horse as a companion for Taylor.

CHAPTER FOURTEEN

RODEO DAYS

During that long year that Darius spent in the shed—cold, damp, and lonely—he barely ate his hay and quickly lost weight. Concerned, Lester called Ben Clayton again and asked for his advice. Ben was surprised to learn the horse had been kept in the shed. It never occurred to him that they would not know what the little horse's needs were. He told Lester that a horse needs exercise and dry ground and that he would come over and help fence in a small yard for him to move about more freely. After being turned out in the small yard, Darius improved. He put on weight, and now along with hay and grass, he was given a small amount of grain, which he loved. Taylor would spend time with him after school, and this helped to decrease his isolation.

Shortly after the one-year contract was up with the BLM, Ben returned to the Bidwells' and told them of a man who ran a small rodeo and could use a horse such as Darius. He would pay a fair price for the horse, and Ben assured Lester that the rodeo man would treat the little horse well. Lester thought this the best choice and persuaded Taylor that her Dusty would be happier with other horses and do well with the rodeo. Taylor trusted her grandfather and agreed to let him go. She had grown overly attached to her little mustang in the year that he spent with them. She talked to him; told him of her dreams, her hopes, her worries, and about her days at school. Darius had become a replacement for the mother Taylor lost a few years ago. It would not be easy to let him go, but she wanted what was best for her horse, not fully understanding that Darius's best interest would be to roam the plains once again.

Ted Harrington, known around the countryside as "Scooter," arrived at the Bidwell's little ranch shortly before noon on a bright, sunny spring day. Scooter was an interesting man. He had risen out of dire poverty during the dust bowl years on the plains. He knew the value of a dollar and had worked hard since his childhood. Scooter had a small string of bucking horses that he used on the rodeo circuit throughout the summer and fall season. He was tall and thin, a quiet man who took to chewing on a cigar most days and who would give up a chance for a meal if there was a dollar to be made. He never had much interest in food for the most part, as there was not much of it available in his family growing up. But he was extremely interested in a horse that refused to allow a blanket to be placed on his back. If marketed correctly, this little horse could make a lot of money for Scooter. He planned to play down the mustang's value to the Bidwell's to see if he could get the horse for almost nothing.

Lester Bidwell might not have known much about horses, but he knew the value of a dollar and stayed firm on his price of $800. He knew about human nature and that Scooter would make a lot of money off his investment, and he also knew that he could not ask for any money the horse might generate in the future. So, without much ado, Darius was quickly loaded onto Scooter's stock trailer and hauled away to the Roaring

Reality Rodeo Show, of which Scooter had a controlling interest.

Confused and disoriented again in the trailer, Darius placed his hooves squarely apart and once again, was able to keep his balance. The stock trailer had open sides with bars for support which allowed him fresh air and he could move about as much as his halter and lead rope would allow. It was a short trip as the rodeo was not far off, about thirty-five miles. Darius was led off the trailer amidst a lot of noise. He was at first hesitant and afraid, but with a bit of encouragement, he let Scooter lead him to the stables at the back of the arena. Darius heard and smelled sweat, grime, a mixture of food odors, well-worn leather, and a cacophony of sounds that made no sense to him. However, above all the din, he heard and smelled horses and let out a loud whinny of welcome. They did not answer back as their need was not as great as his. Nonetheless, he knew they were nearby and marched toward them with Scooter leading him into an empty box stall full of fresh straw and a bale of hay.

Scooter untied the lead rope and went to fetch the horse some clean water from a nearby faucet meant just for that purpose. Darius felt confined in this stall, which was about ten by ten feet. Still, he heard horses on either side of him quietly munching hay as there was a small opening high above him on either side between the stalls to allow for air circulation. When he stuck his head out the door of his stall to look around, the horse next to him stuck her head out as well. She was a large-boned pinto. Seeing Darius, she immediately pinned her ears back at the newcomer and shook her head. She was a no-nonsense sort for sure. Her eyes, one of which was blue instead of dark brown, rolled threateningly at him. Darius withdrew back into his box and stood for a long time, listening to the myriad sounds that swirled around him. Whether from exhaustion or not, he fell into a fitful sleep, first resting one hind leg, then the other. He lowered his head and slid silently into dreams of the wild prairie he had once known.

The next morning Scooter returned to the barns and saw that his helpers had fed and watered each horse. With the addition of Darius, he now had fifteen horses in his string. As this was Saturday, it promised to be the biggest venue of the week. Scooter planned to start the evening's events with Darius to see how he would perform, but first, he wanted one of his helpers to take him over to the loading chute and climb aboard for a trial run. Darius had just finished his grain and was slowly savoring the fresh hay placed in his manger. He was not afraid of the stranger who came to feed him. He had no bad experiences with men but was curious about what this person wanted.

The same man returned with a lead rope and led Darius out toward the arena and the loading chutes where the broncos and bulls in the attached loading pens would wait their turn to enter the arena. Darius followed willingly into the pen and then into the chute a bit more hesitantly. A young man about seventeen years old was waiting on top of the chute for the horse to be loaded. Once inside, the gate slammed shut, and the man dropped quickly onto Darius' back. The little horse exploded immediately, catching his foreleg on the chute's slats. He squealed, tossed his head, and landed hard on the ground. The young man was surprised, not having had a horse react this

violently before. The more seasoned broncs
would stand patiently in the chute, saving their
energy for the explosion that was to come. But
Darius was terrified and confined—two of the
worst things to happen to a wild horse.

The boy quickly settled again on Darius' back. Before he could rear up again, the
side door of the chute was flung wide open,
and Darius saw his escape. He leaped out of
the pen, high in the air, and landed with a
twisting motion, trying to rid the dreaded
thing he felt on his back. The young man was
launched into the air but without the horse
and landed near the wall of the arena. Darius
continued to buck, lurch, and twist as if the
weight were still there. Scooter was flabber-
gasted. His cigar dropped out of his mouth
as he took off his old, dusty black cowboy hat
and wiped his face on his sleeve. What a show
this was going to be!

Darius bucked and galloped around the arena for a few minutes before he realized he had gotten rid of the menace. He stood still, unsure of what to do next. The young man got up, dusted himself off, and limped cautiously out of the arena. Another rider entered, scooped up Darius' lead rope, and led him back to the loading pens. Left alone, Darius calmed down so that Scooter was able to approach him. Scooter knew this little horse was a gold mine. He decided to immediately introduce the paying public to his mysterious bucking horse that no man could tame. *Yup*, he thought, that was an excellent description to draw in the crowds. He would use it as part of the announcer's spiel[20] that evening to see how it went over with the crowd.

---

[20] Spiel: or fast speech or story, typically one intended as a means of persuasion or as an excuse but regarded with skepticism or contempt by those who hear it.

Darius was led back unceremoniously to his box stall, where he spent the remainder of the day slowly adjusting to his new life. He was fitfully dozing when the same man who fed him earlier in the day returned. It was close to dusk as the bright lights came on for the evening's festivities. Darius was led back to the arena's holding pens to where some of Scooter's other horses would be performing in the evening's program. The pinto mare was not among them, and Darius was now meeting these other horses for the first time. They laid their ears back, but otherwise paid him little attention. They were not interested in him as they had their own lives to lead. Some of them were has-been cow ponies and broomtails,[21] picked up on the cheap and taught to buck on command; others, like Darius, were

---

[21] Broomtail: a class of range horses that are considered not worth much.

considered to be a rough string of wild horses fresh off the plains that had been caught and put into service in Scooter's rodeo circuit. Either way, the horses were bored. They had lost most of the energy and spirit that had been a part of their earlier lives. Darius was now part of this mix of second-rate horses. Scooter had decided to save him for the end of the evening and introduce him with a lot of fanfare.

The evening began with each horse led into one of the chutes. The slamming of gates, the yell of the crowd, and the shrillness of the announcer's voice all played a part in making Darius extremely nervous. He milled about the pen, even though the other horses stood patiently waiting their turn in the bucking chute.

When he was the only horse left in the holding pen, he was chased into a chute by one of the men working the arena. Immediately a man dropped onto his back. The chute gate opened, and again, Darius saw his escape and launched high into the air. Word had quickly traveled around the grounds about the new horse Scooter was promoting. Thus, the rider Darius drew by lottery was ready for him.

A bronc rider must stay aboard a bucking horse for a total of eight seconds. It might not seem like a long time unless, of course, you are the one on the horse. The judges then determine the style with which you rode, whether you kept one hand free, whether you rocked your legs back and forth in time with the bucks, and how difficult the horse was to ride. All this played into the judges' decision as to who was the best rider for the evening and could collect the daily prize money.

It did not matter how much or how little the rider knew about Darius; he was tossed almost immediately and sailed unceremoniously through the air as the previous young man had been. During the performance, everyone cheered, hooted, hollered, whistled, and screamed as loud as possible, which only made Darius buck and gallop around the arena even more, terrified and desperate to find a way out of this chaos. Scooter saw dollar signs before his eyes and vowed Darius would be a moneymaker. He decided to call him "Buck" as it was a fitting moniker.[22]

On Sunday, the previous day's routine was repeated. But this time, after the show was over, the rodeo troupe would pick up, load up, and move to another town with some other eagerly awaiting customers.

Darius found his day-to-day life monotonous except for the brief, terrifying periods

---

[22] Moniker: a fitting nickname or description.

in the arena. He took some comfort being with other horses even though they were never allowed to mingle except when in the arena's holding pens. Some of the bucking horses wore saddles, but others, like Darius, were listed as bareback broncs. Scooter knew there was no way he could get a saddle on that horse's back, and even if he could, it was far simpler having him as a bareback bronco.

Word spread fast about the little dun horse in Scooter's rodeo string. No man had been able to sit on his back for more than five seconds. Cowpokes and professional bronco riders started to show an interest in drawing Darius to ride, betting that they could be the first to stay on the little horse. Scooter, seizing another opportunity, decided to personally offer a $1,000 prize in addition to the usual prize money as a challenge for anyone who could sit his horse for the allotted eight-second ride. Scooter's cut of the gate money began to roll in. Large crowds came from all over the county to the rodeo. Some wanted to try their luck with the prize money, and some just wanted to be there to see the show.

Darius did not disappoint.

His terror returned each time he felt any weight on his back. Every time, he sought to escape by charging out of the chute, and if that did not work, at least he would rid himself of the terror by bucking, fishtailing, twisting, and turning to dislodge the person on his back. Because he was small and quick, this was a lot easier for him than it would have been for the much larger horses listed as the saddle broncs.

By the end of the summer season, Scooter took his horses to his winter home on a small spread just outside the town of Indian Springs,

Nevada, on Route 95. Here the horses would remain until late spring, when the rodeo circuit started up all over again. The horses were kept in large pens, separated by mares, geldings,[23] and stallions. Scooter did not see a need to spend money having Darius gelded, which might take away some of his spunk; he surely did not want that to happen.

The horses had no shelter from the piercing winds and biting snow during the winter, but they grew thick, heavy winter coats and huddled together for warmth when the weather was severe. This time for Darius was restful and without trauma. Used to winter's fury, he took comfort in being able to associate again with other horses. But as this kind of treatment hardened up the sturdy and culled the

---

[23] A gelding is a male horse or other equine such as a donkey or a mule that is castrated removing the male hormones so they cannot produce offspring.

weak, Scooter lost two mares that first winter Darius was with them. The mares were older and could not pull their weight at the rodeo; fewer mouths to feed was Scooter's motto.

Spring arrived much too quickly for Darius as the horses again returned to the rodeo circuit. Scooter spent the winter months lining up events for the coming year. It was pretty much a yearly routine; he visited those places nearest to the ranch and then ventured farther afield as the summer season wore on. Everyone knew what weekend Scooter's Roaring Reality Rodeo Show would be in town. Scooter managed the show's bronco riding program and took a portion of the gate money along with the other subcontracted attractions that were with the same folks year after year. The customers who came to the rodeo knew pretty much what to expect from the carnie acts, food vendors, etc.

Scooter loved working the rodeo. It was a good life for him as he had left his wife and two daughters years ago and never looked back. He was never much of a family man to begin with, having little desire to stay in one place all the time. This life was what he loved, and he was good at it too.

News of the new horse Scooter had featured in his string was getting around. People lined up at the gate to buy tickets, and quite often, there was standing room only in the arena. No one was ever turned away. That was not Scooter's style. The more the merrier, he would say, and merrier meant more money.

CHAPTER FIFTEEN

A LAKOTA SIOUX

Darius began his second year with the rodeo full of fear and terror, but this time, he knew the routine as it never changed: morning feedings, lazing about one's stall until late afternoon, getting hauled off to the holding pens, hustled into a chute, a man on your back, bucking your brains out, then being led out of the arena and back to your stall for the night.

This routine went on for most of the long, hot summer. One day, in late August, a lone Native American Indian began hanging around

the barns. He silently watched the horses, taking in their every move. He made himself almost invisible to the workers who were busy with chores—feeding horses, mucking stalls, cleaning bucking saddles, assisting the farrier,[24]

---

[24] Farriers are highly skilled equine hoof-care professionals. They not only fit horseshoes, but they also clean, trim, and shape horse hooves. Farriers work with a variety of breeds in different environments, from riding stables to farms to racetracks.

calling the vet, or whatever else was required to keep horses healthy and active.

Running Feather was a member of the Lakota tribe of the Sioux nation. The Lakota Native Americans were a nomadic equestrian tribe who settled on the South Dakota plains after emigrating west from Minnesota—a proud and dynamic people who hunted buffalo and raised their families in buffalo hide teepees. Theirs was a tragic story after the massacre at Little Bighorn and the Battle at Wounded Knee Creek, when their free and nomadic lifestyle tragically ended, and they were forced onto small Indian reservations by "the white man."

As a child on the reservation, Running Feather knew his ancestors' stories by heart and dreamed of far-off times. As a young child, he liked to chase discarded old feathers stirred aloft by a breeze and given flight as a childhood game, hence his name. He had never been fond of his given name, so as he matured, he chose to be called Earl after an older man who had befriended him and hired him to stack shelves in a local grocery store. Earl, (Running Feather), had not bothered with a surname and was known only as Earl by anyone who made his acquaintance. He was tall and lean and always wore an old, felt tan fedora[25] with a golden eagle flight feather in the hat's wide brim as a reminder of his heritage. He wore faded blue jeans and a white cotton shirt. His shoes were comfortable and sturdy. Down the nape of his neck, there hung a long, shiny black braid, carefully woven each day before he went outside.

~

[25] Fedora: a low, soft felt hat with a curled brim and the crown creased lengthwise.

Earl spotted Darius on his first day at the rodeo. He knew Darius was a wild mustang like those horses his ancestors would have ridden freely across the Midwest and western states' vast plains. To Earl, Darius was known as Tasunka.[26] He instinctually knew the horse must be suffering the loss of freedom found on the plains. He felt this just as surely as the ghosts of his ancestors had. When the rodeo moved from town to town, Earl decided he would follow it as he was interested in the little horse and his compatriots.

The summer dragged on, extremely hot and dry. Each stop along the way seemed the same for the horses. They stayed in musty, wooden, loose boxes, milled around in the high-fenced holding pens to the constant

---

[26] Tasunka: In a Lakota legend, a young warrior sets out on a search for food and instead discovers a creature called horse (tasunka). After the Lakota capture and tame the wild creature they become powerful and full of pride, until the Great Spirit who provided the creatures takes them away.

noise and dust that mingled with a myriad of odors. They ate stale old hay and had sour water to drink. This routine was only interrupted by a few moments of bucking off riders and then long periods again spent in their stalls. Sleep and boredom always took hold of them. Life was not hard, but it was not fulfilling—devoid of the interest that freedom could provide to come and go as one wishes.

Earl watched the horses for hours, leaning quietly against the sidewall of an empty stall, sucking on a sprig of hay. He studied their moods and listened to the soft, comforting sounds as they lazily chewed their hay. He developed a strong interest in their welfare. The workers around the barns paid him no mind, as he was not in their way and was not involved with their chores, and hence created no interest. They were too busy running their daily lives. So, after a day or two, it was as if he was not even there. Toward the end of the summer, however, Earl disappeared suddenly, leaving without a word. No one noticed his absence.

Scooter was busy lining up venues for next year and devoted most of his time and energy to that task. Shortly before the end of the rodeo season, he had his lineup set for the following year. He was satisfied and congratulated himself on his ability to read people and land profitable contracts. He also was able to get a headliner for Buck, who was partly responsible for the ease in obtaining dates for his rodeo horses.

CHAPTER SIXTEEN

RODEO ACCIDENT

Another winter came and went. Darius survived it along with the other horses. Scooter was anxious to begin his rodeo season once again. He did not like the cold, and the added chores and hard work that came with the snow were annoying. He would let most of his help go during the winter, only to hire them again the following year for the rodeo season. He kept just enough men to barely manage the horses and the little ranch for the long winter months.

Earl was aware when the rodeo would begin its summer season. He also made it his business to find out where they would commence their opening act. It turned out to be a town near Scooter's winter homestead. Darius would not have recognized Earl, nor would he have cared about seeing him again if he did. Darius' concern was about staying with his fellow horses and, if possible, out of the dreaded arena.

When he arrived at the fairgrounds, Earl strolled up and down the sheds, checking on each horse, remembering them as he went along. At Darius' stall, he paused and peered into the dark interior to see if there was a horse inside. The small dun was in the far corner, head lowered, weight shifted off his near hind leg, ears relaxed, dozing. He barely opened his eyes to the soft shuffle of Earl's feet outside his stall. Repetition told him that it was not feeding time, nor was it time for the show's noise and commotion to begin, so he looked in Earl's direction, then closed his eyes again, returning to light slumber.

Scooter came by a bit later to check on his string of broncos. He needed to make sure the rehired crew remembered their chores after the long winter. Everything was in order, so Scooter was satisfied they were off to a good start. The routine never changed. Up before dawn, muck out stalls, refill each box with clean straw from the end of the sheds, feed grain all around, break open hay bales and section out to each horse, curry and groom, check hooves for cracks or any problems, fill water buckets. Make sure all stall half doors were secure. There was nothing more exasperating than chasing a loose horse that had found his freedom. Scooter then was off to morning coffee and a cigarette break over by the picnic tables. He was extremely strict about smoking around the barns.

They were in the third week of the circuit when Darius drew an exceedingly competent rider. Jeremy Coggins was a small, wiry nineteen-year-old who fell in love with the rodeo after his dad brought him to one during a father-son weekend when Jeremy was eight years old which was his father's way of connecting with his son after the divorce. Jeremy was not interested in much, including the long, insufferable weekends where his dad tried to act like his best friend. The rodeo was another matter. He loved the excitement, the bright colors, the junk food, and especially the horses as they bucked, twisted, and turned in an attempt to rid themselves of their riders. He thought them courageous, brave, and wild. He wanted to be with them. Over the next few years, he learned all he could about rodeo riding and even spent time studying how the horses and the riders moved in a sort of crazy dance together. His mother was not aware of the amount of time he spent hanging around the fairgrounds, and if she had known he wanted to be a bronc rider, she would have been terrified. A bronc rider usually has his share of broken bones. Some are killed in the process of being either tossed off a horse or trampled on. Lately, riders have chosen to wear chest protection, which has saved more than a few lives.

As it turned out, Jeremy was an accomplished rider, able to stay the eight seconds on most horses. He was thrilled to have drawn Darius' name, as the little horse's reputation had preceded him. Now Jeremy thought he might finally get the National Professional Rodeo Association's attention and maybe get some better rides, earn more money, and make a name for himself. He dared to think he might even get the chance to follow the Pro-Rodeo Circuit and end up competing in the Grand National Rodeo.

Jeremy was all set to go when Darius arrived in the holding pen. He had done his warm-up exercises, spent some time mentally preparing for the ride, and was eagerly awaiting its arrival. Darius knew the drill and was already edgy and jumpy. Reliving daily his life's most terrifying experience was beginning to take its toll on both his body and mind. Once in the chute, he hardly felt the pressure of Jeremy on his back. Most men landed on his back as if to let him know who the boss was. At first, he was confused and hesitated when the chute gate opened. Jeremy was slightly built compared to other young men his age. He had not yet ridden his way into middle age, still trying to make big money on the rodeo circuit, putting on an extra pound or two along the way. Jeremy felt the horse's slight hesitation was to his advantage and seated himself more securely on Darius' back. With that, Darius exploded high in the air, twisted a half-circle, and came crashing down hard on the ground. The horse, whether due to his small stature or calm manner around the barns, was deceptively wild, but Jeremy felt confident. Here was a horse he felt sure he could ride.

~

The longer Jeremy stayed on board, the more Darius twisted and turned in terror. Jeremy began to feel his grip and his rhythm slip. It was then that Darius, without warning, crashed down against the sidewall of the arena with Jeremy pinned underneath him. The outriders on their well-heeled quarter horses immediately sprang into action and galloped quickly across the stadium to the fallen pair. Usually, a horse will get right up after falling because instinct tells him he is vulnerable on the ground and not in control. Darius squealed deeply and then swung his head and neck around attempting to right himself. He could not move.

The strap muscles that supported Darius' right shoulder were injured and had utterly disabled him. Jeremy, knocked unconscious by the fall, was coming to and moaning with the slow realization of what had happened. His right leg was pinned beneath the horse. Two of the outriders immediately jumped off their horses and came to the aid of the boy and the horse. After assessing the situation, they radioed for the vet. It looked like the little horse might have to be shot if he could not get up. Their first order of business was to get the horse off the rider's leg and get Jeremy to the hospital. The gates to the arena swung wide open so that an ambulance that was always on standby could rush in. Jeremy was swiftly and efficiently lifted onto a stretcher, loaded carefully into the ambulance, and whisked away.

By now, the veterinarian hired by the fairgrounds had arrived. He was able to assess that the horse had not torn his shoulder muscle but instead bruised it quite severely and would probably survive. He did, however, doubt the horse would ever be a bucking horse again but said nothing.

Darius went into shock, so moving him was not as complicated as had initially been feared. With gentle encouragement, the men got Darius to his feet as this is what he desperately wanted to do anyway. Standing with all four legs squarely placed, he was breathing heavily but this time allowed somebody to throw a blanket over his back. He was slowly led from the arena and back to the stables. Once in his stall, Darius felt safe and settled down. The vet stopped by to check on him. He gave the little horse an anti-inflammatory injection to help control the swelling that would naturally occur after such an accident. Heat building up in his shoulder caused the pain to increase. The doctor did not want to give Darius any pain medication because this might cause him to move around too freely in his stall. Right now, what the little horse needed was rest and quiet, with a cold hosing of the shoulder area to manage the swelling and giving it a chance to heal. Shoulder injuries are hard to diagnose, so the veterinarian was not entirely sure a tear had not occurred. Time would sort this out.

Scooter arrived shortly and wanted to discuss the condition of his little investment. After a short, hushed discussion with the vet, he realized the horse was probably out for the rest of the season just when things were going so well. Scooter told the vet that "Buck" would get all the care and attention he needed, and he immediately went to work assigning chores to some of the more reliable hired help to take care of everything Darius required.

CHAPTER SEVENTEEN

CONVALESCING

After a week of caring for a sick horse, the stable hands were stressed. Earl had been observing the additional activity around the little mustang and finally stepped forward when Scooter arrived one morning, surprised to see a stranger in his midst. Earl spoke quickly and clearly; he knew he would only get this one chance to make an offer. He asked Scooter if an extra hand would help in caring for the sick horse. Scooter saw an opportunity here but thought to himself, "I

sure don't want this Indian taking me for a
ride." Earl understood Scooter's thinking and
assured him he was not offering his services for
money. They quickly agreed to terms, and Earl
settled in with Darius. He now spent most of
his spare time near Darius' stall. Darius quickly
adjusted to Earl's presence and began to look
forward to the man's company each morning
like he had with little Taylor Bidwell, a time
that now seemed so long ago.

Earl cleaned Darius' stall, brought fresh
hay and grain before the other stable hands
arrived in the early morning hours. He was
careful not to give him more fodder than the
other horses received as it did not take long
for him to figure out how Scooter's mind
worked when it came to finances. However,
he did give Darius extra time, extra massages
to the injured shoulder, and extra cold-water

hosings. When their tenure at a fairground was over, Scooter's team moved on to the next venue, taking extra care when it came time to load Darius onto the stock trailers. At the new location, the fairground vet came to check on Darius. When the horse had healed enough to begin exercising the shoulder muscles, Earl was willing and ready to lead him around. Darius grew to enjoy these sojourns with Earl in contrast to spending all his time in his stall. Earl was silent like other horses would be, but when he did speak to Darius, it was in a soft, deep, and slow voice just meant for the little horse. Darius followed him willingly, and a great trust began to form between the two. If, while on their rounds, something caught Darius off guard and he shied, Earl would stay extremely quiet and still so that Darius would learn from his example.

Scooter began to see an improvement in his horse and was thankful he "had found" Earl, for he counted himself the one responsible for the meeting. Although Earl was dependable, Scooter had been raised not to be too sure with *Indians*. For his part, Earl knew not to trust white folks too much either, but for now, he was enjoying his companionship with Darius.

Of course, Scooter was anxious for his horse to recover, hoping he might be able to salvage some revenue from Darius during this year's run. It would never occur to Scooter that his horse would never be a professional bucking horse again. As the horse had survived the initial accident, Scooter was sure he would once again *"buck for bucks,"* as he loved to say. For this reason, he was willing to let Earl continue working with his horse.

The days of summer slowly evaporated, and it was time to return to the homestead before the arrival of the cold weather. Scooter approached Earl to see if the Indian would agree to be one of the regular stable hands. Earl was more than pleased to tag along with the horses as it would give him something to do for the winter. As a result, Darius had less attention at the ranch, with Earl now required to help with the other horses.

Spring arrived wetter than usual, with everything covered in mud. It did not take long for the crew to get fed up with the mess. It was hard walking, hard keeping things clean, and the horses that were shod had their iron shoes sucked off soon after they had been applied. Before long, however warm tentacles of spring spread across the fields, and things slowly began to dry up. Trees full of sap burst forth with their lacy green finery, first with buds, then leaves. Scooter hoped Darius was fit to go back on the circuit and insisted that he come along with the other horses. Earl vainly tried to keep him back at the ranch to rest some more, but Scooter was insistent.

During the early weeks of the rodeo season, Earl disappeared as suddenly as he had appeared. Scooter had come to depend on him and was angry about his departure. It was three weeks before Earl reappeared. The stable hands besieged him with questions and accusations. Earl was mute as usual and would only speak to Scooter. He explained to his boss that he had spent several weeks making inquiries of his tribal members about a place where cast-off, discarded, and spent wild horses had a suitable place to live out their days. Scooter looked perplexed. Why was Earl telling him this? It was then that he learned the truth about his Buck's real condition.

The little horse would never again feel terror each day bucking frantically in an arena. His shoulder injury had afforded him this unexpected freedom. He was not able to buck as before, and his shoulder inhibited his movement so that he could not gallop and frolic as before. If one looked closely, there was a slight hesitancy to his shoulder muscle when he walked. It seemed to twitch after his foreleg hit the ground. There was no pain anymore because Earl, with all his diligence and determination, had done the best for Darius, but he could not remake the mustang into the grand bucking horse he had once been.

Scooter, not happy about the outcome, had to digest and sort this all out. After all, this horse was supposed to be his ticket to a prosperous and comfortable life. Scooter was not a hard or cruel man, despite all his faults, and in his way, he loved his horses. He did not want any harm to come to his little Buck. The following week, Scooter called Earl into his temporary office at the fairgrounds and told him to make arrangements for Darius to go to Earl's uncle's spread and be turned loose with the other mustangs.

CHAPTER EIGHTEEN

A SOLUTION

The sun rose hot and dusty on the morning of Darius' transfer to the Native American lands. Earl arrived early to clean his stall. He gave him extra feed, even if Scooter was watching. He curried and brushed the little horse until his dun coat shone and glistened. His thick mane and tail took a bit longer to clear the tangles and "tail ropes," those long horse hairs that seemed to twine around each other into what could only be called a rope. The farrier came one last time to check his hooves. Wild mustangs never need their hooves trimmed due to the shape of the hoof and the rough terrain over which they roam.

Darius sensed something was different in the way the humans around him were behaving. Change always made him nervous and jittery. Earl saw this, gently rubbed the horse's forehead, and was able to calm him down. He hired a little two-horse trailer, pulled by his uncle's old 1954 Chevy truck somehow kept in skeptical running order all these many years. Darius was not sure about the narrow, dark entrance to the trailer. He hesitated, then backed up. Earl did not force him forward as he understood the uncertainty behind Darius' movements. He was patient. There was no schedule to follow, so he gave the horse all the time he needed. Earl worked slowly, offering encouragement so that he finally and willingly loaded on the left side of the two-sided trailer—the better side to use when only one horse is on board. Fresh hay was waiting in a hanging net for Darius. The stall sides were thickly padded and helped keep him standing firmly with the truck and trailer's movement.

Earl was excited to get on the road, away from the hurly-burly of the rodeo. He was taking Darius back to the land where he truly belonged, land belonging to the Lakota Sioux from which their ancestors had been separated so many centuries ago. The trip was long in the dusty trailer, and it took two days to reach his uncle's range. When Earl arrived, his uncle, brothers and sisters, mother, and cousins were waiting patiently for him. A little ceremony was held with the arrival of each new horse. They had collectively sought out and retrieved twelve horses for a life of freedom on the 3,500 acres their uncle had acquired for just this purpose.

After greeting his family, Earl—again called Running Feather—backed Darius out of the trailer and onto a blustery hilltop. Darius raised his head high, his ears locked forward as he drank deeply of the clear air swirling around him. Then without warning, he let out a shrill whinny that shook his whole being. He tossed his head but waited patiently for Earl on the other end of the lead line. Sensing his urgency, Earl led him quickly to the gate that connected the fence line encircling all 3,500 acres. Here, the horses would be safely enclosed but mostly unaware of the borders. Once inside the gate, Earl whispered a few words, *yušká ayuštáŋ,* then ceremoniously removed Darius' halter and lead rope. It only took a minute for Darius to realize he was free. As before, he hesitated, then leaped into the wind to own his freedom, and galloped away down the slope

before him. He whinnied as he ran, sometimes stopping to listen, then moved off in the direction where Running Feather's uncle knew the other horses would be.

Darius was now *Tasunka*.

He was home.

ACKNOWLEDGEMENTS

Not only have many individual horses allowed me to share their lives, but family, friends and professionals have willingly guided me on this wonderful journey of writing my first book.

Alice Schertle, author of The Little Blue Truck series, graciously agreed to read my first draft and encouraged me to get it published. Susan Pearson, a children's book editor and author of many books such as "How to Teach a Slug to Read" gave me sage advice based on her experience.

David, my wonderful husband, was always there to encourage me when my confidence waned or disappeared altogether. He was my sounding board and would sit patiently through copious readings of drafts and editions.

Self-Publishing School (SPS) with Chandler Bolt was immensely valuable in providing me with the tools for writing, editing, and publishing. I could not have accomplished this without his fantastic team or the many marvelous self-publishing authors I met along the way.

Michelle Gano was my coach at SPS and was always there for me with encouragement and positive suggestions. Many others on the SPS team who are too numerous to count held a unique place in my journey.

ACKNOWLEDGEMENTS

Ebook Launch was instrumental in polishing my cover design and editing my story. Andrea Reider of Reider Books offered her talents to design and format my final draft.

And then there are all those past authors and illustrators of horse stories that I read as a youngster who influenced me and sat quietly on my shoulder as I wrote my story and brought my little mustang to life.

For all of you and many more, I am deeply grateful.

ABOUT THE AUTHOR

Susan Metcalfe Honneus is an artist who has been drawing for most of her life. Her parents would give her blank sheets of drawing paper which she would then divide into six sections and draw a horse's story in each section.

Summers were spent at her grandparents' farm. Her grandfathers gave Susan her first horse, a wonderful bay Morgan named Ginger. Since then, Susan has lived with many wonderful horses. She has loved them all - their inquisitive personalities, as well as their mischievous traits.

Susan graduated from Skidmore College with a B.A. degree in Art and Art History. She is an active member in the American Wild Horse Campaign, Skydog Sanctuary, and the Guild of Berkshire Artists. She is married with two grown children, stepchildren, and a variety of grandchildren and great grandchildren. She lives in Western Massachusetts with her husband, David, on her grandparents' farm where her horses run free in the pasture.

Susan developed a lifelong interest in the natural world around her learning to recognize different bird species, flowers, trees, and insects. She enjoys drawing birds, horses, and people's pets. Check out her web page, www.meadowbrookgallery.com, for her artwork.

Passionate about the welfare of the wild horses out West, she wanted to bring a story about a wild mustang to life. "Into the Wind" is her first book.

Made in the USA
Coppell, TX
01 September 2022

82456880R00100